# MISSION
# CATASTROPHE

## Nottinghamshire

Edited By Machaela Gavaghan

First published in Great Britain in 2019 by:

Young Writers
Remus House
Coltsfoot Drive
Peterborough
PE2 9BF
Telephone: 01733 890066
Website: www.youngwriters.co.uk

# FOREWORD

Young Writers was created in 1991 with the express purpose of promoting and encouraging creative writing. Each competition we create is tailored to the relevant age group, hopefully giving each student the inspiration and incentive to create their own piece of work, whether it's a poem or a short story. We truly believe that seeing their work in print gives students a sense of achievement and pride in their work and themselves.

Our Survival Sagas series, starting with Mission Catastrophe and followed by Mission Contamination and Mission Chaos, aimed to challenge both the young writers' creativity and their survival skills! One of the biggest challenges, aside from facing floods, avoiding avalanches and enduring epic earthquakes, was to create a story with a beginning, middle and end in just 100 words!

Inspired by the theme of catastrophe, their mission was to craft tales of destruction and redemption, new beginnings and struggles of survival against the odds. As you will discover, these students rose to the challenge magnificently and we can declare *Mission Catastrophe* a success.

The mini sagas in this collection are sure to set your pulses racing and leave you wondering with each turn of the page: are these writers born survivors?

# CONTENTS

| | | | |
|---|---|---|---|
| Kacey-Mai Linford (11) | 65 | Joseph Clark (14) | 105 |
| Katie Mae Harrison (11) | 66 | Eylul Sen (13) | 106 |
| Jack Conroy (12) | 67 | Hamza Tran (13) | 107 |
| Summer-Leigh Smith (11) | 68 | Rhiannon Pearce (13) | 108 |
| Yasemin Iclek (12) | 69 | Hollie-May Jones (13) | 109 |
| Megan Levy (12) | 70 | Jessica Shaw (13) | 110 |
| Mia-Lorrae Davies (12) | 71 | Loretta Nkomo (13) | 111 |
| Shaun Chiutsi (11) | 72 | Jennifer Quarcoopome (13) | 112 |
| Milly Griffiths (11) | 73 | Tiarnna Karim (14) | 113 |
| Faith Cumberland (12) | 74 | Renai Rikki Dayes (13) | 114 |
| Alex Luke Hoult (12) | 75 | Trisha Taurai Saxby (13) | 115 |
| Zoe Leah Streets (11) | 76 | Myles Peet (13) | 116 |
| Bethany Aleesha Woodland (11) | 77 | Maksymilian Reczkowski (13) | 117 |
| Ashton Lang (11) | 78 | Connor Ford (13) | 118 |
| Emmanuel Elliot (12) | 79 | Sam Casey (13) | 119 |
| Thomas Hardstaff (11) | 80 | Qamar Akhtar (14) | 120 |
| Kelcie Lie Cornell (11) | 81 | Adelia Hunter (13) | 121 |
| Caitlin Louise Hemsley (12) | 82 | Satvinder Kaur (14) | 122 |
| Shakira Reid (11) | 83 | Zara Brittain (12) | 123 |
| Harrison Boughton (11) | 84 | Iola Hall (12) | 124 |
| Ashton Jelley (12) | 85 | Joe Bakewell (13) | 125 |
| Daisy Sims (11) | 86 | Ethan Crofts (13) | 126 |
| James Jackson (11) | 87 | Nila Mobushir (13) | 127 |
| Elissa Clark (12) | 88 | Broderick Liam Christman (14) | 128 |
| Jordan Hammond (11) | 89 | Bailey Leek | 129 |
| Lily Wolfgang (11) | 90 | Tiago Pinheiro (13) | 130 |
| Abigail Mai Taylor (11) | 91 | Ameer Adam Rabhe (12) | 131 |
| Finley Smith (12) | 92 | Toby Clingan (13) | 132 |
| Sadie Owen (12) | 93 | Chelsea Beniston (13) | 133 |
| William Robert Campbell (11) | 94 | Kyren Skermer (13) | 134 |
| Mason Hennessy (11) | 95 | Cane Hyland-Wells | 135 |
| Dylan James Devonshire (11) | 96 | Lacie Harrop | 136 |
| Libby Orton (11) | 97 | Toluwalase Adewumi (13) | 137 |
| Milan Minorics (12) | 98 | Mabad Ul-Hassan (13) | 138 |
| Thomas Joseph Noone (11) | 99 | Logan Norman | 139 |
| | | Peace Animashaun (14) | 140 |

## The Nottingham Emmanuel School, West Bridgford

| | | | |
|---|---|---|---|
| | | Max Pawlowski (13) | 141 |
| | | Tanzeela Tabrez (13) | 142 |
| Lara Phillips (13) | 100 | Zach Spindler (13) | 143 |
| Thomas Watson (13) | 101 | | |
| Bella Chineme Nwaneto (14) | 102 | | |
| Ben Lunn (14) | 103 | | |
| Albert Gudmunsen (13) | 104 | | |

## The Samworth Church Academy, Mansfield

| | |
|---|---|
| Olivia Grace Harding (13) | 144 |
| Kady Weedop (13) | 145 |
| Imogen Hursthouse (13) | 146 |
| Arabella Neve Radford (13) | 147 |

## Wilsthorpe School, Long Eaton

| | |
|---|---|
| Kiera Flynn (12) | 148 |
| Alex Twigg (12) | 149 |
| Hannah Jenkins (13) | 150 |
| Ruby Davies (11) | 151 |
| Melissa Louise Bowers (12) | 152 |
| Alex D'Arcy (13) | 153 |
| Amelia Parker (12) | 154 |
| Scarlet Burnell (12) | 155 |
| Phoebe Warwick (11) | 156 |
| Eli Enzo Beard (11) | 157 |
| Isobel Jane Eyre (11) | 158 |
| Daisy Smith (13) | 159 |
| Zoe King (12) | 160 |
| Amélia Tuck (13) | 161 |
| Sophie Louise Morris (13) | 162 |
| May Longmoor (12) | 163 |
| Maisie Booker (12) | 164 |
| Yasmin Jade Johnson (13) | 165 |
| Izzy Johnson (13) | 166 |

THE MINI SAGAS

# Lost

Light blinded me. "Wake up! Are you alright?" My eyes fluttered open. I was unusually warm, my cheeks damp with tears. "You're the last one." He looked at me, eyes piercing blue. "Your planet collapsed," he continued. A sudden deep silence. Everything I knew was lost.

"I-" I tried to speak but words wouldn't come out. "Ssh, preserve your energy. We're almost in the new world now." I acted as if that made sense but to be honest, I had no idea what that meant. All I knew was I was alone, alone and lost...

**Eve Eugenia Heatlie (13)**
Hollygirt School, Nottingham

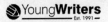

# 3091

3091, the year our central government called for mass annihilation. The central government was our brain and operated everything on Earth. Even they didn't predict the sun exploding and leaving half the world in a vast landscape of scorching, pulverised mess, the other half, that's where I am, waiting to get swallowed up by the flames of the dawning sunlight. There's no point in telling you who I am, what I liked and disliked, because I only have moments to spare. Standing near the extinction of humanity, I open my arms, embracing the beauty of destruction...

**Emma Leu (13)**
Hollygirt School, Nottingham

# End Of All Ends!

Sweat starts to appear. The countdown begins. I, Emma Ware, have started my journey. You haven't heard what's going on? Earth is being sucked into a disaster, a black hole! Every family is traumatised so I'm here to prevent this monstrosity. I've just left the Earth's atmosphere and may never return. Millions of thoughts swim through my head as I approach the Black Devil. Me and the team came up with a strategy to put the machinery in place. I put myself forward to lead. We venture out into the unknown  Suddenly, a blinding light...

**Hamna Zeeshan (12)**
Hollygirt School, Nottingham

# Survival

Philip jerked awake, he'd been unconscious in his taxi. Recovering, he stared around and saw a corpse. Terrified, he leapt out, but that was a mistake. As soon as he was out, a herd of zombies ran at him. Terrified, he ran for it.

Hours went by, minutes, seconds, it was hard to tell. Finally, he heard honking in the distance. He went there but it was just a zombie trapped in a car. He had nowhere to go, they were going to get him. He looked down, ready for the biting to start, then he saw the bite mark...

**Leo Ware (11)**
Hollygirt School, Nottingham

# Death Valley

It was just an average day in Orlando when disaster struck. This frightful cataclysm had occurred numerous times previously. The gale became increasingly intense. It was unbearable. People came out of their homes to see what was happening but were immediately whisked away into the dancing funnel of the wind. Roads, buildings, trees and vehicles were ravaged until they were unrecognisable. The remaining survivors clung to their families, waiting for their lives to be snatched from them. The roofs caved in, they couldn't last any longer. This dreadful hurricane had made its way around the world, killing off humans forever.

## Isabella Bennett (11)
The Garibaldi School, Forest Town

# Trapped In Winter

Perishing, icy wind gusted towards the two climbers. "Let's get out of here!" George yelled, his voice muffled under his scarf.

"We're nearly at the peak! Just a few more steps," Fred bellowed.

"Argh!" George screamed, petrified. They ran as fast as they could, their hearts beating like drums. The peak was now pure rock and all the snow was in a big ball and was gaining speed. They dodged out of the way and the humongous snowball missed them narrowly.

"All of the snow has fallen from Mount Everest, trapping the world in winter," the news reported...

**Lana Bramley (11)**
The Garibaldi School, Forest Town

# Catrina

The wind blew hard. It wasn't the usual calm, quiet night, babies screamed as they watched their houses being ripped to pieces from their car window. Dogs howled as they saw their owners being squished by their own houses. Evaline had platinum-blonde hair and sea-green eyes.
"Everyone jump into my plane. We'll fly to a safe place!" Evaline was the town's mayor. When she moved into the town, this happened. "It's Catrina," said Evaline.
"But she's not supposed to hit us!" shouted a town member.
"I know." All of a sudden, the ground opened up...

**Lydia Shaw (11)**
The Garibaldi School, Forest Town

# Vicious Vengeful Venice

It was an average day in the wondrous city of Venice, birds swooped high in the clear sky, civilians meandered across the crowded streets and the silent canals were untouched. Unexpectedly, miniature ripples formed in the water and within seconds, the busy streets were neglected. Everyone stood on the bridge as if it was luring them in.

Five minutes passed, the ripples were four times larger than before and the water started to rise. Unbelievably, a colossal wave over fifty metres tall emerged and before the people could even think about escaping, the iron bridge collapsed and death struck. Silence...

**Luke Spencer (11)**
The Garibaldi School, Forest Town

# Himalayan Hell

I was relaxing in my small log cabin, watching the skiers do their thing when suddenly an explosion-like sound came booming down the immense mountain. I swiftly stepped outside and then my brave and happy personality left me in a flash. An enormous avalanche was cascading down the mountain's summit towards us. There was a sudden explosion of crashing rocks, as well as screaming loud enough to shatter windows everywhere. Everyone was running and stumbling around, attempting to escape from this disaster. But I didn't. I froze. I stood on the bloodstained snow and waited, then I was taken.

**Bobby Lacey (11)**
The Garibaldi School, Forest Town

# The Heatwave

I'm stranded in an absolutely tragic rainforest as there was a heatwave that wiped out the world's population. This is the only place I can hide in shelter. Venus crashed, knocking the sun closer to Earth and it's disintegrating anything in its path. So now I'm stranded here, with nothing except myself and aliens. But look on the bright side, I've discovered intergalactic life! But then at the same time, I'm probably going to die. I'll either die from hunger, thirst, aliens or insanity, yay! A great, big, sarcastic yay! Now I should probably look for some food...

**Benjamin Oliver (11)**
The Garibaldi School, Forest Town

# The Disney World Disaster

The sweltering sun rose out from behind the Disney castle. The believers knew this was going to be a hellish day. Little did they know, it was going to ruin their 'perfect' vacation. The sun had exploded and the untouched kingdom had caught on fire. In the space of thirty minutes, the entire park had been engulfed in a ravenous flame. All the rides stopped with an unexpected jolt. Terrified screams filled the atmosphere as families sprinted in all different directions, trying to leave the unforgettable nightmare. The castle had now been reduced to a smouldering wreck of rubble.

**Emily Jane Severn (11)**
The Garibaldi School, Forest Town

# The Flood

It happened so fast, one minute I'm plodding through heavy rain, the next I regain consciousness falling, surrounded by azure water on every side when suddenly, I stop. My vision clears, my hands tremble, the feeling of isolation consumes me. Everything is gone except water, only beautiful, deadly water stretching for miles, killing everything in its path. In the distance, I catch the sight of a blood-soaked man weeping next to a miserable young girl. I rush over to assist but it's too late. She's lost. I feel the man's sorrowful screams but he is also a dead man...

**Kieran Witham (12)**
The Garibaldi School, Forest Town

# The Unfortunate Events

*Bang!* Dark winds hammered against people's humble abodes. Screams of children, men and women filled the air. Silence struck. The earth started shaking. Lady Liberty tumbled. Commotion soon restarted. That was the day New York changed. The only remains were the rubble of houses. The wind gained the power of a thousand men. The catastrophe had struck millions of houses and animals. A man yelled for help as his daughter lay under the remains of his house. No one helped, they were dealing with their own problems. The wind gained power, then another big disaster happened...

**Olivia Stafford (11)**
The Garibaldi School, Forest Town

# Earth's End

The embellished house trembled in fear. It maliciously shook from verge to verge whilst a fractured wall was tugged from the uneven stretch of green. Unexpectedly, the fragmented windows were violently shedding glass all over the cobbled streets. Adam started running anxiously. His nerves wracked beneath his pale skin. Suddenly, the deafening shouts and screams erupted the town. Out of nowhere, Adam came to a sudden halt and carefully examined his surroundings. Black smoke filled the periwinkle sky but before Adam could take another step, three mysterious figures surrounded him...

**Calum Gunning (11)**
The Garibaldi School, Forest Town

# The Devil Strikes Again

Ten years on, I still remember it so clearly, the terror, the horror in this once beautiful city...
As I walked hurriedly along the bustling, familiar streets wearing my best designer suit, little did I know the Devil was devising a horrific attack. The skies turned black and the ground began to rumble. Seconds later, giant jets of lava burst up the river, smothering New York in torrents of glowing liquid. The blood-curdling screams of people drowning in the boiling lava were terrifying. Frozen in fear, I stood helpless in my scorched shoes and ragged suit. Would I survive?

**Joshua Cullen (12)**
The Garibaldi School, Forest Town

# The Circle Of Devastation

Something about today was a little less pleasing. Was it the putrid smell that wandered the hallways or something else? The sky seemed dingy and ominous-looking, clouds hovered above. Taylor saw mighty winds targeting buildings and people in an attempt to destroy them. Devastation circled the city and faces full of fear filled the streets. What was once a perfect paradise turned into a place with a helpless disaster that they called a hurricane. She dashed out the building in an attempt to save as many innocent lives as she could. The real question was, could she keep her own?

**Bebe Aurora Davies (11)**
The Garibaldi School, Forest Town

# The Takeover

Calmly, I pondered through the streets taking in the refreshing air. At that moment, I felt relaxed. Shining brightly, the sun beamed down upon my shoulders, then it hit us. The air was thickening within seconds. My chest felt hefty, I ignored it. The minutes went by. The air grew hotter, scorching us. Our skin burnt to a crisp. The streets were as silent as death. As people were collapsing, hospitals were crammed. There was no help available! The human race was in danger. A crisis! I wasn't sure. I decided to strul through the streets but unfamiliar figures appeared...

**Niamh Riley (11)**
The Garibaldi School, Forest Town

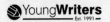
# The Devastating Disaster

I was nonchalantly strolling down the icy path, my fingers numb. The sludge squished underneath my boots as I continued on. All of a sudden, there was a deafening crash. Pandemonium spread throughout my village! The pungent smell of burning wood was alarming. Screams flooded out from every direction, surrounding me in a heartbeat. As I breathed in a breath of apprehension, I could taste the scalding lava from the volcano. The sight of people running was horrific. I felt the suffocating ash in the air. A colossal boulder shot out of the volcano. I lay still, afraid, alone...

**Allyssa Wardle (12)**
The Garibaldi School, Forest Town

# Fear Fills My Heart

It was an average day, birds were tweeting, kids laughing, it was nothing out of the ordinary, but then an ear-piercing siren started ringing. "What was that?" I asked myself. My body trembled through the door. Horrifyingly, a colossal wave was storming towards me! I cleaned my spectacles to make sure I wasn't dreaming. I scampered to the window and dived through it. I was as unnerved as turtles out of their shells.

A few seconds later, after I'd closed my eyes in terror, it was a worldwide bloodbath. I fell asleep in trepidation, then I woke up...

**Scott Atkinson (11)**

The Garibaldi School, Forest Town

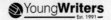
# The Flood In The City

Rain was thrashing down, the sea was mental and the waves were getting higher and hovering towards us. People screamed. People cried. One colossal wave leapt on us! The city was like a giant water bottle slowly filling up. Towers and statues were floating. The water was running across the city, abolishing everything in its path. It was uncontrollable, it was chaos! Everyone was choking on salt water, trying to fight the taste but we couldn't. No one could. It was going, but it was still there. The water finally passed, leaving us with nothing but death and rubbish.

**Ashlie-Jade Wagstaff (12)**
The Garibaldi School, Forest Town

# The Avalanche

It was Christmas Day and well-wrapped presents were being opened. Suddenly, the news flashed on. 'Breaking news: An avalanche is flying down the French Alps, run whilst you can!' Outside, people were running as fast as they could. When we saw what they were running from, it was a sight you couldn't unsee. A ginormous, icy, pearl-white cloud was hurtling down towards us. We ran, our feet pounding against the frosty floor below. All I could hear was the muffled screams of the people being devoured by the frosty giant. Suddenly, I fell. I never woke up again.

## Gabriella Smith (11)
The Garibaldi School, Forest Town

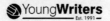

# It's All Over

I went for another tiresome day at work. "Woah, what was that?" I enquired wearily. The earth shook as rapidly as my washing machine on a quick spin. I began running to the stairs but I didn't make it in time. I collapsed on the floor, the earth was vibrating more than ever now. I gripped hard onto the railing, waiting for destruction to unfold. I opened my eyes, it wasn't shuddering anymore. I rapidly ran downstairs. There were odd creatures everywhere! I overheard a girl scream. She ran up to me and we rushed outside. Disaster was all around...

**Benjamin Greenley (12)**
The Garibaldi School, Forest Town

# The Canyon's Demise

Luke trudged through the ankle-high snow as the bitter wind scraped against his face like a dagger. The quaint, picturesque village he dwelled in was located in an immense canyon. Every day he would collect wood, but today contrasted from the others. First, it was a shudder. Then the blanket of snow formed into mounds. Then the cataclysm began! Then he realised. It came... faster and faster! The avalanche came at a phenomenal pace. He ditched the wood and sprinted, adrenaline tingling, coursing through his veins. Luke tripped, then braced himself. Then silence...

**Jimmy Allen (12)**
The Garibaldi School, Forest Town

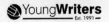

# The Flood

As the tide slowly started to settle, the devastated looks on people's faces suddenly turned to a face of relief, relief that they'd survived, relief that the tsunami was over. Although it seemed to be finished. As people were ready to cautiously go down the hill, they realised that their whole city was flooded. The sight was terrifying. The whole city had a quilt of dirty seawater over it. The sight of dead bodies floating around was scarring.
As time went by, you could see the Statue of Liberty plunging down, then the Empire State Building sank...

**Skye Regulski (11)**
The Garibaldi School, Forest Town

# It's Happening Again

It was horrible, everyone was screaming, running and crying. I was only a kid at the time. Whenever I go to sleep, I get flashbacks. It's scary, it's like it's going to happen again. Then I see it again. *Bang!* "What was that?" I look out of my window, smoke's coming out of a big hole. I run outside, people are screaming. I have thousands of flashbacks. I am so scared, it's like the Purge. All I can see is red. I run inside. "Mum, are you okay? Argh!" I see blood splattered across the room, then I hear something...

**Bailey Aaron Thomas (12)**
The Garibaldi School, Forest Town

# The Earthquake

I let go, falling into the dark abyss. Upset, numb, cold, I suddenly flashed back to when this catastrophic event occurred...

It was the year 2054 in Nepal. As I watched the news, they suddenly reported the largest earthquake happening in *my* city. My heart stopped. *An earthquake!* I started to panic. Suddenly, I shook. It was coming for me. I froze. My house split in half! I fell. Luckily, I grabbed onto the ledge, holding on for dear life.

A couple of minutes passed, I let go, falling into the dark abyss, upset, numb, cold, lonely...

**Riley O'Callaghan (11)**
The Garibaldi School, Forest Town

# The Earthquake

I gazed out the window. I saw a building collapse in front of my eyes. It was silent at first, then all I could hear was screams, the screams of children, parents, everyone. The ground started to shake. Books and TVs started to fall. Everyone was running, trying to escape. Babies were crying so loud, it was unbearable. The ground dropped. The halls packed with people. I was squished against the wall. I couldn't move. The ground dropped once again, dropping like a lift. The hotel crushed to the ground. Screams got louder. Then silence. No one made a sound...

**Holly Taylor (11)**
The Garibaldi School, Forest Town

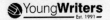

# A Disastrous Day

The hot Arizona day with everyone relaxing under the sun turned disastrous. As the ground was rumbling and shaking, black smoke covered and filled the air with toxic gases. Everyone shook with fear, people were frozen. That was until the volcano erupted and everyone and every living thing was running for their lives, screaming for help. Ash and lava ripped through the land. People couldn't breathe properly so they slowed down, but what they didn't know was that the molten hot lava would devour everyone. The whole state ended up covered in hot, grey ash.

**Jack Orton (11)**
The Garibaldi School, Forest Town

# Category 6

I awoke shrieking to an excruciating pain with no awareness of what was happening. My seven-year-old self felt weak, bewildered. I glared out of my dust-filled window and then a tsunami of terror flooded my mind. A single tear slid down my pale, grey face. A colossal hurricane whipped around and took the land around me. I could sense it was over. *Smash!* The sheer power and force collided with me. It felt like it consumed my drained, helpless soul, the intense amplitude all around me, it felt ceaseless. And then my deceased corpse lay there, rotting...

**Reece Reed (11)**
The Garibaldi School, Forest Town

# The End Of Life

First, it was the newspaper, then suddenly the whole world knew. Heatwaves began, this was a heatwave like no other. This could wipe out the human race! The sun had exploded. This caused drought, the fishing lake didn't have a single drop of water left. The ground was bone dry. Extreme weather caused ear-splitting sirens to constantly sound as the weak were falling like flies. Flaming hot fires started to spread, dead trees were burnt to black, cold ash. This time no one could escape, no matter how hard they tried. The human race was eliminated at once.

**Keira Riley (12)**
The Garibaldi School, Forest Town

# The Unknown

I remember it vividly, the screams for help, cries of pain, lifeguards running, frantically trying to figure out a plan...

Dozing off peacefully on a Saturday, I heard the noise, the thunderous, deadly noise. I glanced over to see waves crashing and huts flying. Screams of terror came from a little girl, waves flew around her. She wouldn't make it alone. I ran. I reached her, a shadow was cast upon us. It was a colossal, blue wave as clear as day. I realised nobody was there to say goodbye, nobody could see us drifting out into the deep unknown...

**Millie Harpham (11)**
The Garibaldi School, Forest Town

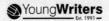
# The Smoke Spread

The huge volcano was meant to erupt over a hundred years ago but it hadn't done so...
It happened on an unusual, cold day. It started normally. I got up, did some work, my family were farmers and so was I. Suddenly, there was shaking in the ground, then flaming lava, then the darkest of smoke. The volcano had erupted! People were screaming and began to flee. The smoke had spread across the world, choking everything in its path, removing life. But I didn't have to live in a destroyed world anymore because I was dead, like every other creature.

**Aimee Riley (11)**
The Garibaldi School, Forest Town

# Death Valley

It was the first full day of my expedition in the Sahara Desert, located in Egypt. At about ten in the morning, me and my group were getting ready for a hike. As I strode onto the porch, my foot started to smoulder. Quickly, I frolicked back. Yesterday, when I had rambled in, it wasn't that blistering!

Five minutes later, out of the corner of my eye, I caught a glimpse of a blazing inferno heading straight for our village! Fearing for my life, I darted outside to warn everyone. Then I sprinted to switch on the news. 'Extreme heatwave...'

## Mason Brown (11)

The Garibaldi School, Forest Town

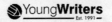

# Coming To The End Of Life

Peacefully, I sat in my rocking chair relaxing before I moved, then I heard a commotion. I thought nothing of it. Unexpectedly, the window flew open and the roof flew off. With my face in shock, the cottage started swaying from side to side, making me feel ill and dizzy. Progressively, the howling became louder, the cottage started to fly up and took me along with it. I solemnly thought to myself that my life was going to end here. My heart beat wildly against my chest, fleeting thoughts rushed through my mind. *Nowhere to run, nowhere to hide...*

**Mackenzie Armstrong (11)**
The Garibaldi School, Forest Town

# The Ferocious Hurricane

There was an uncomfortable sensation of heat in the air. Sweat dripped down my face. Unfortunately, the weather was about to change dramatically. We were all too indulged in our lives to realise. It came with a powerful rush. A vigorous gust of wind whipped the streets maliciously, most of the cars were ripped apart. Another painful force of wind blew harshly into me. It felt like I was being stabbed. Then I saw what was causing it. A huge hurricane was heading my way, throwing anything that got in front of it. It was merciless and full of ferocity...

**Harry King (11)**
The Garibaldi School, Forest Town

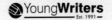

# Death Is At My Door

*Boom!* That's the sound that changed my life forever...
It was a usual day in my hometown of Nebraska. Everyone was off on their holidays and I was sat in the peaceful corner of my sitting room when a piercing howl burst my eardrums. I tried to steady myself as I trembled terrifyingly towards the window. "What's going on?" I asked myself, but I had no answer. I opened my door and a flurry of wind blew me off my feet. It was a hurricane! Before I could move... *boom!* An apocalypse hit and wiped out Planet Earth.

**Francesca Lily Grace Caulton (11)**
The Garibaldi School, Forest Town

# Tsunami Terror

As the scorching hot sun hit down on the city, the humongous skyscraper stood tall, guarding the city and the crystalised beach but before long, people knew something wasn't right. *Boom! Crash!* The whopping, colossal wave gathered into a wall of blue, crystal water to be thrown onto thousands of people. As the people walked, distraught, they all started to run, screaming and praying for help. The wave scattered across the city, leaving buildings crashing down and lost, frightened families waiting to find out where their loved ones were.

**Cerys Young (11)**
The Garibaldi School, Forest Town

# Heatwave Fury

My palms were sweaty. The sky was burnt-orange. All eyes were stuck on the sun surrounded by fire. The pavement was cracking, ready to explode with fury. No one knew what was happening. Babies were screaming with terror and parents were dashing around, not knowing what was happening. Adrenaline was running through my mind. No one could travel because the roads would shatter. Everyone turned inaudible so I listened to the sound of sizzling. Unexpectedly, the ground that had cracked began to shake. All of a sudden, something came out of the ground...

**Sienna McGrath (11)**
The Garibaldi School, Forest Town

# The Unexpected Event!

It was an unusual day in New York, then the ground started shaking. Buildings were crumbling and there was a screeching noise that lasted hours.

Approximately one hour after the earthquake, a teenage girl named Maddie was found in a collapsed house, with nearly no injuries. Maddie slipped out from under the table and was shouting for her parents. From the corner of her eye, she noticed her dad crying and holding her mum's hand. Slowly, she sat down and hugged him. He said, "As long as we have each other, we'll be alright."

**Keva Halfpenny (11)**
The Garibaldi School, Forest Town

# Hitler's Plan

Hitler just did the unthinkable, he unleashed the Devil across the world. I am in New Zealand and I've just discovered that the hell of Yellowstone has erupted in California. I am one of ten citizens left to wander this so-called utopian Earth. There is an airport on Kazama Mountain, where I can obtain a flying mechanism and propel to Iceland and kill Hitler...
I have landed. I think Hitler's power of Hell will overpower me. This is probably the last you will hear from me so I will say, I will try to overpower Hitler's weapon...

**William Emmerson (11)**
The Garibaldi School, Forest Town

# A Volcanic Twist

I expected to wake up to the birds chirping raucously at the morning sky but no. Instead, I got the sound of people screaming outside my window. I ignored it at first but the screams turned into crashing. I sprinted to my window to see the horrifying sight of scorching lava flowing just seconds away from my house. I knew there was nothing I could do about it so I sat in my bedroom, waiting for this nightmare to be over. Suddenly, it all went black as the words 'Game over!' appeared. I sighed. "Now I'll have to start over!"

## Hannah Wilkinson (11)
The Garibaldi School, Forest Town

# Blanketed In White

The sharp wind struck across my face. Dagger-like, the snow was falling quicker than before. The people surrounding me were dropping like flies, surrendering to the avalanche. I should have fled. I had to stay. I couldn't just leave them. As I went up the steep hill, it started again. Drifting faster than before, I let myself fall...

When I opened my eyes, I saw nothing. I was trapped, unable to move from the mounds of snow above me. Trying to move was unbearable. As the bitter cold crept up my skin, it was burning me. I was stuck...

**Taylor Jones (11)**
The Garibaldi School, Forest Town

# Hawaiian Hell

People melted on the sunbeds of the beach under the Hawaiian sun. People started screaming, people started crying. Waves of heat could be seen by the naked eye. The bubbles of the ocean could be felt by the swimmers as they let out the screeches of Hell. The sand, now harbouring small fires, burnt the feet of the islanders as they walked. It was a complete wipeout, except for a couple of blistering people, struggling, reaching out for help. Suddenly, a blinding light shone from the horizon, but no one remained. The worst heatwave had struck.

## Kiera Louise Skinner (11)
The Garibaldi School, Forest Town

# The End

I woke up startled by a peculiar rumble. It got louder. Finally, it stopped. "Phew," I said as I was still drained of sleep. Suddenly, my mum burst into my room screaming and bawling at me to get up. Still feeling like I'd taken a sleeping pill, I proceeded to pull on my clothes and gaze through my window. All I could see was scorching hot lava rushing towards us as if its life depended on it. The ash clashed with the clouds and meteors flew everywhere. Unexpectedly, I heard a strange whine and then my whole roof collapsed...

**Krzystof Malota (11)**
The Garibaldi School, Forest Town

# Shifting

The house trembled. It forcefully shifted from verge to verge until it tore the wall from the ground. Miles stood, unable to move due to the nerves wracking beneath his skin. The house shook more vigorously. That is when Miles ran. He ran faster than he'd ever run before. He came to a halt and examined his hometown. The sky was black with smoke, there was wreckage and fallen bricks everywhere, and fire. Earth oscillated but this time, there was only darkness. The house above him had fallen. There was nothing, only darkness, only death.

**Joshua Mews (12)**
The Garibaldi School, Forest Town

# The Heatwave

It was terrible! How could this ever happen to me? The earth beneath me dried up, cracking from the blazing rays of the blinding sun. My skin blistered, my hands swelled and my throat was sore from dehydration. Desperate for water, I continued my journey to find something to drink. I felt alone. I had nobody by my side. All of my family were gone forever. In the distance, I could see the ocean calling out to me. Carefully, I began to run. Knowing I couldn't go any further, my feet collapsed and I fell to the blistering, sandy ground...

**Olivia Brooke Devonshire (12)**
The Garibaldi School, Forest Town

# Contrasting Denouement

The unbearable sight widened as the shadow crept closer, flakes of snow dashing over me, making me defenceless. "Denouement is near!" I listened to those words. My independence bled out of me, nothing was left of what I had. Why was I here? Feeling lamentable, I stopped to realise the avalanche was an inch away from me, like dust drifting into the wind, piercing through my pure heart. Curious, I stepped closer. Death came, destined to come to my tar-like feet. *It will not get me.* It was too late. "Help, help!"

**Kayleigh Ann Jewkes (11)**
The Garibaldi School, Forest Town

# The Death Quake

It was an ordinary day. However, it wasn't. It had been a few hours since the tragic news was plastered all over the globe about the earthquake. The wind was crisp and whipped you like a piercing smack in the face. Cement grounds cracked, trapping the lives of the humans inside. Children howled for help, cold sweat dripping down their foreheads. I dashed, protecting myself under the wooden table. My heart thumped rapidly. The hairs on my arms stuck up like lightning. The door had been violently thrashed down. Was I the only survivor?

**Lily Thomason (11)**
The Garibaldi School, Forest Town

# A Tragic Avalanche

On the 25th December, Christmas Day, a storm hit Antarctica. The storm was tragic...
It was a perfect day, blue sky and white clouds. All of a sudden, it went dull. Everyone was screaming. A mother grabbed her child saying, "Get away!" The snow started to fall, people started to scream. People locked themselves in their homes. Fifty-two people died, a hundred got injured. Luckily, twenty people survived unhurt. This was a tragic storm with few survivors. It was a shocking, terrifying storm. The survivors were shocked.

**Sophie Humphrey (11)**
The Garibaldi School, Forest Town

# A 'Hole' Lot Of Zombies

*Bang!* There were explosions next to the comic shop. Out crawled a zombie with sci-fi lasers. Immediately, tanks came but as they came out, the zombies moved location. As they caught up, there was a hole of zombies! The great war, man Vs zombies. Mad Max came in and threw grenades at the monsters. The hole had eaten into Florida. What would happen next? Max jumped in and found the boss cloning the zombies! The army jumped down and shot the clones but the boss ran away. From behind, the army was killed. Max threw a grenade...

**Myles Jake Dalby (12)**
The Garibaldi School, Forest Town

# The Flood That Drowned The Human Race

I didn't know what was happening...

Earlier today, I heard a wave of water outside so I went to have a look. Silence. The village of Plain was flooding! All I could hear was the sound of children screaming. Then it hit me from head to toe. I went cold. As I began to swim, a brick hit me on the head...

As though I had woken from a nightmare, I sat up. "Hello?" I screamed. No reply. "Help, I am hurt!" As silent as death. Then I heard a noise. It sounded like a person. I definitely wasn't alone...

**Indianah Eve Davidson (11)**
The Garibaldi School, Forest Town

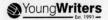
# Left Alone

It was picture-perfect - the mountains, the city, everything except the streets. Screams and shouts sprinted through the thick air of the morning. The ground was shaking furiously, knocking people off their feet. It became hard to breathe. I tried to open my mouth to yell but before I could, massive, black rocks fell from the sky. Before I knew it, orange lava spilt over the top of the volcano. I turned and ran until I reached the bay, the lava on my heels. The boats were all full, only one was left but just then, it pulled away...

**Isobel Dobson (12)**
The Garibaldi School, Forest Town

# The Tsunami Attack

It started as an ordinary day, the sun was out and people were sunbathing on the beach when something random happened. All of the water got sucked up and people didn't know what was going on. Everyone stood up and they all looked straight towards the beach. When they stared at what was going on, they saw a humongous wave heading towards the town. The wave was no ordinary wave, it was a tsunami! Everyone legged it off the beach and ran through the town. When the tsunami hit the town, it hit the buildings like a wrecking ball...

**Thomas George Harris-Chamberlain (11)**
The Garibaldi School, Forest Town

# The Volcano News

Four people are sat in the living room. Suddenly, Summer runs in. She then tells them that a volcano is about to erupt outside any minute. They all grab their things and dash for the door. Tears splash down one of the girls' faces, everyone looks at each other. One of the girls looks confused, then explains to the others that a volcano wasn't ever in London in the first place. Cautiously, they all push open the door. A man jumps out, a camera crew behind him. Everyone gets a surprise when they find out it is for fake news!

**Alix Barke (12)**
The Garibaldi School, Forest Town

# Gone With The Waves

I had woken up damp with sweat. No, dripping. I got to my feet, shrieking for my parents. No reply. I wasn't surprised to find their dead bodies outside. I returned to the bunker, not closing the doors. I crouched in the corner reading then began hearing footsteps, they became louder until they were behind me. I felt the knife pierce through me. My corpse lay on the cold, hard floor. Not all stories have happy endings.

This was the story my brother told me before the tsunami hit and killed my family. Gone with the waves.

## Gia Stonehouse (11)

The Garibaldi School, Forest Town

# No Oxygen

Rodger opened the air-locked space shuttle. Gently and lightly, he set foot on the moon. It was flat, the air was still. Craters began to appear. Out of the blue, an abandoned space station appeared. Obviously, Rodger had to check it out. Rodger tried to open it but it was stuck so he pulled out his gun and shot it. It opened this time. As he took a step in, he saw a blue alien lying on the cold, metal floor. Rodger didn't think twice. Green ooze was everywhere. Rodger's oxygen began to run low. He panicked, breathless...

**Joshua Moss (12)**
The Garibaldi School, Forest Town

# Wales-Cane

"This is news reporter Martha calling from the south of Wales. A really bad storm, well hurricane, is heading this way. If you are listening, you need to go down to the police station and go underground ASAP! Make- you br- your prec- wh- you go. Please try to tell other people about this. Our brave officers will come round the houses and pick you up. I- you- haven- g- cars. This is really bad timing because tomorrow is Valentine's Day but all of our belongings will be gone. News reporter Martha, calling off now."

**Sky Elizabeth Dixon (11)**
The Garibaldi School, Forest Town

# Sunfall

No one was to be seen, no children playing, only lifeless bodies. Well, not all. There was one survivor. It came out of a secret lab. The building crashed to the ground as it came out. How could it have survived? Unless it wasn't human. What if it was an alien or a robot? It was stacking up the dead bodies. Suddenly, the ground started cracking and the dead bodies fell through the floor. The sun fell but that thing was still alive. It slipped onto the broken floor and before it could look up, the maniac doctor fell next...

**Khya Louise Lewis (11)**
The Garibaldi School, Forest Town

# Hurricane Hell

The sky fell dull upon this beautiful New York City day. Screams screeched through the streets. Swarms of birds burst out of the horizon as if their lives were about to end. Then it struck. The wind whipped in front of my eyes. I felt my life rip away from me. For a split second, I was within an inch of my life. The streets were dead, bodies flew away, cars weren't even able to resist this powerful force wreaking havoc through the city. Death had come to claim its victims  The roads of this once great city were chaos...

**Jake Hart (11)**
The Garibaldi School, Forest Town

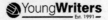
# The End

Screams echoed through my mind as we dashed for the safehouse. Dana and I could see it clearly now. It reminded me of a ring of fire with a tiger coming out, but instead of a tiger they were monster-like creatures crashing down, making the ground rumble with each one, forcing the ground to crack open. Dana unlocked the door, a sweet sense of safety overcame me as I stepped inside. *Safe at last*, I thought to myself.

It had been an hour when we heard it, the thing grabbed Dana and flew off. I chased after it...

**Sienna Lucy Massey (11)**
The Garibaldi School, Forest Town

# A Tragedy In Spain

It was a weird and strange day in Salaca on the coast of Spain. People were having fun on a busy beach. A young boy called Marane De Gea was surfing in the sea when some strong winds came and wiped him out. At that moment, he knew that something was going to happen. The wind got stronger so he told his mum, "If we don't go now, we could die."

"Okay!" his mum replied. And he was right...

An hour later, the wind got really strong. People started to get sand in their eyes and became blind...

**George Lees (11)**
The Garibaldi School, Forest Town

# A Cold Breeze

I switched off my TV when a breeze arose from below. It was about to happen. I packed my items: a protein bar, rope and my knife. I put on my jacket, then my window smashed. The closest shelter was a mile away. I swiftly scattered through, the cold penetrating my hands. There were large arrays of lost souls trapped in the clear ice. It was raining sub-zero ice, slicing my skin. As I reached the shelter, the ground shook. A large statue collapsed, crushing the exit. I was bleeding, my arm was trapped. I fell, bleeding...

**Samuel Gilman (11)**
The Garibaldi School, Forest Town

# The Earthquake Stole My Family

The ground rumbled as if it wanted food. I questioned my parents, "What is that shaking?" They responded, "It's nothing."

*Phew*, I thought to myself. Then I realised my parents were attempting to remain calm, which made me anxious. It was getting bigger when I realised it was an earthquake! The house began to get torn down. We ran swiftly until a roof chucked itself down onto us. We all collapsed.

I rose from my slumber, not knowing anything. I realised I was all alone...

**Amelia Slowinska (11)**
The Garibaldi School, Forest Town

# The Storm

With a crooked neck, I rose, violent rain pounding onto my window. I then sprinted to the kitchen, already hearing the siren blaring. I desperately reached for anything I could. Suddenly, hearing waves, I feared for my life. I stared out of the window and saw my neighbours on the next street being overtaken by the waves and mercilessly killed. I ran for my life to the bunker but it wouldn't shut. I broke down, facing death itself. Crying, I looked at the roaring tsunami as it broke down glass. My eyes then shut...

**Jed Randall (12)**
The Garibaldi School, Forest Town

# One Survivor

Let's take a flashback to the bad days, the days that I can remember and will never forget...
It was all my fault. It all started when I was out skiing with my best friend. My plan was to scare him so badly that he would never forget it. Well, my plan worked well. He screamed. Unfortunately, his scream rattled the snowy mountains until we heard the crumble of a mountain. We gazed up and saw snow falling off the mountain. It swiped us off our feet. At that moment, It was the end, the end for my best friend.

**Kacey-Mai Linford (11)**
The Garibaldi School, Forest Town

# The Hurricane

It was mayhem. The hurricane was killing the weak and the elderly! We were all protected by our underground homes because of the utter chaos above. It was no surprise, a hurricane in Florida, but no one had ever experienced one like this before. Yesterday we were all happy and playful, not knowing the horrors of tomorrow which were yet to come. Dad shouted from across the safehouse, he was going to check up above. I told him not to, I knew it was going to happen. He was gone. Gone into the depths of the hurricane.

**Katie Mae Harrison (11)**
The Garibaldi School, Forest Town

# The Avalanche Monster

I was climbing up the mountain, my spiky boots digging into the edge. Getting closer with each step I took. It felt like a touch away, but realistically I still had a long way to go. I was looking for a monster everyone was talking about. I was halfway there but there was still no sign of a monster. I was getting achy and tired but I still went on. Three-quarters of the way there, the next thing I knew, a massive snowball was falling. I climbed down so quick, I was back at the start. But then... *roar!*

**Jack Conroy (12)**
The Garibaldi School, Forest Town

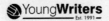

# Crushed

The previous, beautiful, blissful city had turned into a dilapidated mess as if it had been abandoned for years. Getting up, Jamie and Jasmine scrambled to their feet even though they were hurt and they didn't know where their parents were. Their mum and dad saw their children, grabbed them and took cover on high grounds. As the ground started to shake again, buildings collapsed within seconds, harming several others. Not getting away in time, their mum and dad got crushed. What would they do without them?

**Summer-Leigh Smith (11)**
The Garibaldi School, Forest Town

# The Avalanche

I loved having fun with my family. It felt like everything was going so well. I stood for a minute alone and blurred out what was happening. I thought to myself how lucky I was to be with my family. I carried on playing on the mountainside. Everybody suddenly looked up into the sky. My heart sank into my stomach. I panicked. I heard screams. I saw large amounts of snow pouncing down towards us. More was crashing down. Everybody was scared and frightened. I felt disorientated...

I stood up, I was alone...

## Yasemin Iclek (12)
The Garibaldi School, Forest Town

# Beware Of The Floods

There she was stood in aisle 9 of Walmart, deciding on whether to have mint chocolate chip ice cream or chocolate when all of a sudden, the lights started flickering. They called over the loudspeaker, "Everyone go to the top floor!" She dropped the shopping and ran. Then there was a blackout. She didn't know where she was. She ran in a straight line and came to the stairs. At this point, she had got to the third floor. The water was up to her knees. She was going to die if she stayed there...

**Megan Levy (12)**
The Garibaldi School, Forest Town

# The Sun Will Change Us Forever

The sun was rising. It got hotter and hotter. I heard the floor growl. I looked outside, there was a crack. I shouted, "What is happening?" I went outside. The water was even hot, it could scald your skin. "Help!" People were dying left and right. People were screaming for help. It was just getting hotter, so hot it could crack your skin. The cracks in the ground got bigger, people howled in agony. People were sacrificing themselves. "Please stop this, I'm suffering..."

**Mia-Lorrae Davies (12)**
The Garibaldi School, Forest Town

# A Volcanic Issue

Joyful times, out and about playing, then *crash!* Straight into a wall. I was unconscious. All of a sudden, the ground began to shake. *Boom!* Pieces of magma shot into the air. I began to wake up and hesitated instantly. My instinct was to run straight away but I was attracted to the volcano until fire began to spread. I headed straight for the forest as lava caught up to my trail. The only thing I could do was find shelter. I blocked up the entrance of a cave, but then the lava came...

**Shaun Chiutsi (11)**
The Garibaldi School, Forest Town

# A Plane Catastrophe

It was really busy at gate thirteen, everyone was getting ready to board the plane. It was time to board, everyone got on the plane. It was time for safety checks, then they could jet off. The plane was on the runway, then *zoom!* It shot off into the air. The plane was now far up in the sky. They were two hours away from their destination. The plane was just about to go over a volcano when *boom! Bang!* The volcano erupted. The plane went crashing down to the ground. They were all dead.

## Milly Griffiths (11)
The Garibaldi School, Forest Town

# The Deadly Tsunami

The crashing of waves is in the distance, today is sunny. I'm happy just sitting in the sun. I can hear the sound of happiness going in and out of my ears. There's a really big wave coming. I want to go in it but Mum won't let me. I think it's the biggest one yet. All the surfers are going in but they're not coming back out. My sister went in there, I hope she's okay. All of a sudden, I can see no more. I am in the water. I cannot see anything. Everything has been wiped out...

**Faith Cumberland (12)**
The Garibaldi School, Forest Town

# The Eruption

As smoke gushed out of the volcano, a stampede of people panicked. A booming explosion happened and lava started to course down the slope. Cars were devoured by the lava. Without warning, I leapt out my chair to look outside. The news wasn't wrong. The lava was almost at my house so I dashed out the back. I heard civilians screaming as they were consumed by magma. It was a nightmare! Hundreds of people died that day but luckily, the people who lived rebuilt this once sacred place, people like me.

**Alex Luke Hoult (12)**
The Garibaldi School, Forest Town

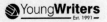

# The Climb

I staggered through the snow. It was misty but I carried on. I couldn't help but notice something was different, tranquil but piercing nonetheless. Suddenly, an immense amount of crisp air came at me at an alarming speed. I hit the floor with a bang. Cautiously, I got up. Then I noticed something in the distance. I stood as still as a statue, due to the shock. Scared to the bone, I ran. A sharp, glossy rock... I was aware it was there but I fell, as usual. Before I knew it, I was in a body bag.

**Zoe Leah Streets (11)**
The Garibaldi School, Forest Town

# A Disaster

It was an angry, cold winter's night. The wind was blowing off the snow and going everywhere. This was a disaster! Me and my friends went walking through the village. It was so windy it was hard to see. This was an awful avalanche! We could hear someone's voice coming from somewhere but we didn't know who it was. We had a look, it was a person who was injured. The person was crying, someone from their family had died because of the avalanche. It was on the news, it was a disaster...

## Bethany Aleesha Woodland (11)
The Garibaldi School, Forest Town

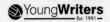

# Extinction

Everyone was enjoying a warm, summery day. It was 32 degrees and the temperature spiked up by 30 degrees in a few seconds.

Minutes later, entire cities were on fire as citizens scrambled to lakes and seas to stop the horrific pain of burning alive. People watched from a distance as the kilometre-tall, orange arms tried to grab the clouds. Within hours, the human race had been reduced to a mere eight hundred inhabitants. Families said their final goodbyes to each other as they watched...

**Ashton Lang (11)**
The Garibaldi School, Forest Town

# The Waves Came

It had passed. *What do I do?* I charged down the rusty stairs causing sounds of death, enough to deafen the ears of a baby. Water drowning my shoes, I rushed to the other skyscrapers to scavenge for things. "Hello?" shouted a timid voice from inside. *Do I respond or do I flee?* Trapped, there were many shouts coming from the building. I hid. My friend was already dying. I gave him all the medicines I could, but death overcame him. I had to fight for my life...

**Emmanuel Elliot (12)**
The Garibaldi School, Forest Town

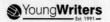
# The Eruption

The plane took four hours. I was going to the lab in the morning.

In the morning, I got a taxi to the lab. It took forty-five minutes to get there. When I got there, I went up to the volcano to find the special rocks to get the diamonds. Suddenly, it started shaking. I had a sudden thought. I froze. I began to run as fast as I could. The smoke puffed everywhere. Lava poured everywhere. I could feel the heat from the lava. It was close. I jumped on the closest rock and climbed...

**Thomas Hardstaff (11)**
The Garibaldi School, Forest Town

# An Early Earthquake

Windows shattered, floors rumbled, my bed rocked from side to side. Shaking, I put on the clothes I'd been wearing for the past few weeks. Like a cat being strangled, I heard a never-ending scream from the distance. My body shook. I raced outside to see my mother lying there right in front of my eyes. My heart sank. I picked her up and raced to my father but there he was, lying there too. I fell onto my knees. My eyes filled with water. I knew that I had to get out of there...

**Kelcie Lie Cornell (11)**
The Garibaldi School, Forest Town

# A Summer's Day

Once upon a time, there was a town called Mansfield. There was a catastrophe coming, news reporters had been saying there was going to be a heatwave tomorrow so Dad filled my pool up so I could cool down after my hike with Uncle Ben. Today was the day. I was going on my hike. Finally, I reached the top of the mountain. I was about to burst into flames. Just after Uncle Ben caught up, we heard the bushes sizzling like they were about to give way. Then I saw the flames...

**Caitlin Louise Hemsley (12)**
The Garibaldi School, Forest Town

# A Catastrophe In Brazil

An enormous flood had come. There were at least ten people left, I thought. I smelt and felt the salt rising before me. All of a sudden, I lost someone. I was devastated. I cared a lot about them, they were... family, and family is everything. The water was rising so I thought I'd risk my life to get my mum. I dived in as her face went cobalt. I went back, I was the only one who could look after my tiny brothers. I was really scared that I would lose them both in the flood...

**Shakira Reid (11)**
The Garibaldi School, Forest Town

# Work Disaster

I was in my office doing some work when all of a sudden, there was a loud crack outside of our workplace. Everyone thought it was the powerbox exploding because all the lights went out but when the electrician went to go fix it, he ran back inside screaming that we were all going to die. He told us to look outside. We did what he told us to do but when we looked there was a huge, pointy rock that looked like a volcano squirting magma out of the top, and it had started rising...

**Harrison Boughton (11)**
The Garibaldi School, Forest Town

# The Flood

The unthinkable just happened. It hit. Everything was flooding, all the shops, houses, fields and schools. It was mayhem! It had broken down houses until they were just piles of brick. It was only me left. What could I do? It was dark and all of the street's lights had gone out. I had no place to stay or to be safe from the flood so I found lots of old bricks and built a hut. As soon as I put the last brick on, a huge wave hit and knocked it over. Life was almost over...

**Ashton Jelley (12)**
The Garibaldi School, Forest Town

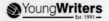
# Why?

It was a peculiar day. Very strange. Nobody saw it coming. It all started when the floor got hot, burning even in my small, poor town. Then something came out of the ground a few weeks later. It was red and orange with black marks. Again, very strange. Something horrid happened that day. The burning fire. It was tragic. So many people died. I had to do something about it. That's when my mind clicked. Face-to-face with the lava, I thought, *why did they dig it up?*

**Daisy Sims (11)**
The Garibaldi School, Forest Town

# A Windy Morning

One day, a man called Joe Bill was on a walk but then his best friend, Tyler, said for him to run. "It's coming!" Joe looked behind Tyler to see a stage-five hurricane destroying the buildings and others running. He ran as fast as he could but he saw a man stuck in his car. He stopped to break the car window and pulled him out because he couldn't be selfish. He saw a building made from red brick with no windows. He ran inside but the hurricane got to him

## James Jackson (11)
The Garibaldi School, Forest Town

# Danger's Coming...

I was at home but little did I know my life would never be the same. The first thing I heard was the sudden drum of a white drift ploughing down the mountain. As I walked out of my house, I had no idea that I had put myself in so much danger. The snow poured down the straggled mountain and it roared like a hyena pelting down a road for food. My ears bled, they were in excruciating pain. All of the screams were hurting my eardrums. All I wanted to do was get out of there...

**Elissa Clark (12)**
The Garibaldi School, Forest Town

# The Car Explosion

Early one morning, a family of five were bored. They tried to find something to do. Then they heard a bang. They all got up and looked out the window. There was a gang outside. They all had guns and they were pointing towards the car's petrol tank. They shouted, "Come out or I will pull the trigger!" They all came out and went to the car but then they pulled the trigger. *Bang!* The car blew up. The car flew up into the air and the whole family died.

## Jordan Hammond (11)
The Garibaldi School, Forest Town

# Other Words

It was a cold night. My window was open wide and the eerie breeze blew strongly. I was watching TV. Suddenly, the news came on and they said something about a volcanic eruption. *Probably fake news, there's a lot around here.* Suddenly, I heard a large clap of thunder. I soon realised it wasn't. Right then, two women came through a portal that seemed to have come from another world. At that moment, they explained that the fate of the world was up to me...

**Lily Wolfgang (11)**
The Garibaldi School, Forest Town

# A Catastrophe In Spain

I looked all around me when the ground started to rumble. I rushed home to see if Charlie was okay but all I could see was a puddle of blood in the middle of the floor with him in it. I was heartbroken. What if I had been there? Out of the gloom, the ground split in half. Would everyone be okay? I decided to go to the nearest airport to get out of this mess. I decided to travel to London to see our godparents to explain what had happened to Charlie, but my life ended...

**Abigail Mai Taylor (11)**
The Garibaldi School, Forest Town

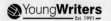

# The Earthquake At 10 Downing Street

"Here at 10 Downing Street, the PM is about to make an appearance. Wait... the ground is shaking. It's getting more violent. The PM is inviting everyone into number 10... Everyone is under chairs or desks. It has turned into an earthquake! Back to the studio!"
"I hope everyone is okay! The studio is shaking now. The computer is falling! This is BBC Radio 1. *Fuzz.* We will be back after the catastrophe." *Fuzz, fuzz, fuzz...*

**Finley Smith (12)**
The Garibaldi School, Forest Town

# An Awful Avalanche

Today I decided me and my friends would go on a walk. It was a normal day until we walked past an avalanche. The snow started to crawl down the mountain. People were screaming and shouting. I heard the snow as chunks hit me. When I ran my hand down the mountain, I felt the mountain crack. I saw people crying, I could smell the fear on people. I could taste the dirt of the mountain. I needed to do something so I decided to go home. I dragged my friends with me...

**Sadie Owen (12)**
The Garibaldi School, Forest Town

# Gas Mask 13

I'm Nishigal Tasumi, I was in an asylum. There was a tsunami, thirteen people got hit. I was one of them. They said we were dead, that our bodies couldn't comprehend the radioactive water, but it actually changed us, our minds. We now have animal instincts. They only let us out to fight wars. All we did was kill, some of us drank the blood. I wore a gas mask, it was covered in blood. They called us back in. I didn't listen, I ran away to the city...

**William Robert Campbell (11)**
The Garibaldi School, Forest Town

# The End Is Near

The ground started to rumble and the volcano erupted. It destroyed all the forests and the city of Mexico, making all the skyscrapers fall. The screams were louder than the helicopters above them. The houses were burnt down to a crisp. Only a few people were alive at that point. They tried to escape the country. They were basically racing the lava. The volcano's smoke covered all the windows of the cars and steamed them up. Would they make it out in time?

**Mason Hennessy (11)**
The Garibaldi School, Forest Town

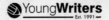

# The Water Waves

I was just sat in my house when I heard screams. The day before, I was near the sea when I saw a storm. I ran as fast as I could but I still got poured on. That was the worst day of my life, but today was even worse because the water had come closer to our city. I wished I was somewhere else. But instead, I had to be in horrible Brazil. Then a message went out. "The flood is on its way!" The water covered the city. The world had ended, it was over.

**Dylan James Devonshire (11)**
The Garibaldi School, Forest Town

# Coco

It was 12pm in Jamaica. Since Monday, it had been more than sixty degrees. It was unbearable for the people, animals and the trees. Then there was a bang. Someone had fallen to the floor. Then within seconds, everyone and everything had died from the blazing sun burning their bodies.

Two days passed and only one thing was fighting to stay alive. It all came down to one animal to stay alive: the dog, Coco. Would Coco be able to stay alive?

**Libby Orton (11)**
The Garibaldi School, Forest Town

# The Avalanche

It was cold in the evening. I was playing on my Xbox with my mum and dad downstairs. All of a sudden, I heard a big crash outside and with all my might, I sprinted down the stairs as fast as I could. I saw my dad on the floor with the sofa on him and my mum covered in snow and water. I asked my mum if she could help me lift the sofa off Dad. We lifted the sofa and he was alive because of it! We survived the mighty avalanche.

**Milan Minorics (12)**
The Garibaldi School, Forest Town

# Broken Shelter

I was sat there as still as a rock, relaxed, feeling like sleeping when suddenly there was a noise. Suddenly a fireball struck, making me jump out of my skin! I ran like the wind to what appeared to be an abandoned underground bunker. As soon as I entered, I saw several people standing there, gazing at me like they'd seen a ghost. My heart skipped a beat as the vent exploded, releasing volcanic ash into the room...

**Thomas Joseph Noone (11)**
The Garibaldi School, Forest Town

# Again And Again

Stepping onto the bumpy path, the ground shudders beneath me. Everyone topples over. Repeatedly, the ground rumbles again and again. A loud silence claims us. Shrieks and screams break the silence. *Crack!* Unconsciously scrambling to my feet, I stumble backwards. The tall, glass tower leans forward, forming black shadows like death looming over its victim. Sprinting away from the toppling tower, a crowd rushes off down a road. Children cry, families split, some accept it, like death. *Boom!* "Down!" Everyone drops like flies as a wave of ash covers us. There's no sound except the aggressive ringing in my ears...

**Lara Phillips (13)**
The Nottingham Emmanuel School, West Bridgford

# When The Big Apple Became Ephialtes

Albert Alzheimer, overly arrogant, intellectually superior, a bio-physicist pioneer, led the Dimensional Rift Voyage project. A genius, with an opinionated ego, bespoken by his unspeakable actions of initializing the Rift Voyager, bound our world to Dimension 13, providing an entrance for beastly Settlers to stampede through, jerking us Into war. This extended for nine years in which I, Henry Taylor (scientist), served in the army until streets were littered with the trash of rotting corpses.

The scientist's plans to dissect the Settlers was halted by Albert, who, lusting for power, transformed himself into a Settler!

## Thomas Watson (13)
The Nottingham Emmanuel School, West Bridgford

# Mankind's Unseen Mistake

Life was a greater struggle than ever for mankind as the flood couldn't be solved easily. It wasn't a child's playful mystery game, only an unsolvable catastrophe. Humanity had grown to an unthinkable size, Earth overflowed with humans, leaving only miniature spaces. There was no more room to build houses or farms, very little food to reach hungry children. There weren't enough jobs to earn money while the percentage of claustrophobic people increased to a ridiculous amount. Scared, starving, the Devil had gifted us with this torture. Mother Nature had turned her back on us. What should we do?

**Bella Chineme Nwaneto (14)**
The Nottingham Emmanuel School, West Bridgford

# Channel Tunnel

"Take refuge underground! Meteor showers approaching!" the radio announced. Suddenly, I was hurled into a mob of screaming people and we were forced into our place of refuge. The Channel Tunnel...

Currently, I am huddled in my torn clothes. There's two million of us in the tunnel, with only basic provisions. The deadly meteors rain down, crashing down and shaking our place of solitude, causing the utmost fear for everyone. This is hell on earth. Suddenly, a ragged-looking man appears from the gloom. "I bring news," he says, "very bad news." All eyes look to him...

**Ben Lunn (14)**
The Nottingham Emmanuel School, West Bridgford

# Living In Red

Molten rock creeps out from every crevice. Muttered murmurs bubble under the thick layer of fiery sea. These grotesque creatures swarm and devour anything worthy of destruction. Except him. He stands trembling like a petrified mouse above the shadows, face as white as snow, waiting in death's eyes. But death never comes for him. "The first in years!" people had cried. "He is the chosen one!" Day after day, week after week, he stays, insisting on defeating the lava fish, their bulging eyes and venom-spitting weapons. Nothing can survive but he does, but it's never over...

**Albert Gudmunsen (13)**
The Nottingham Emmanuel School, West Bridgford

# Nowhere Is Safe

The tsunami had hit. Every city was underwater and hardly anyone had survived. Only the mountain climbers survived. This apocalyptic world was surely the end of England. A submarine scanned the underwater city, it had only two people in it. The submerged buildings tumbled down, almost in slow motion. The monstrous tsunami hadn't hit America so everyone had to try to get there. However, the only vehicle that was working was the submarine, which meant the climbers were stranded, no communications, no food and they had nowhere for shelter. A huge storm was on its way. Nowhere was safe...

**Joseph Clark (14)**
The Nottingham Emmanuel School, West Bridgford

# Mum!

In a small cottage on the edge of a cliff, it was just Rooney and her mother. It was a peaceful day, or so they thought. The kettle stopped boiling and the lights went off. What was happening? *Rumble.* "Argh!" Rooney peered out of the window, trees were collapsing and people were running. An earthquake! Another rumble, the cliff started to shake, cracks appeared throughout the floor. Rooney on one side, her mother on the other. The cliffs were collapsing! Rooney quickly grabbed a piece of rope and threw it to her mum.
"Rooney!"
"Mum!"

**Eylul Sen (13)**
The Nottingham Emmanuel School, West Bridgford

# Disease B9RY5

An advanced metropolis, nothing could stop New York. With highly-developed military and technology, nothing could penetrate our defences. Despite this, I still built a reinforced bunker, and I am happy I did...

The disease was a force of nature. It was in the air. When inhaled, it released acid into the vital organs and was attracted to the scent of humans. Because of this, after a while, it evolved and deteriorated most materials, it destroyed my sign: *Jenson's home*. By now, most of the population have been exterminated but the disease still thrives off humans...

**Hamza Tran (13)**
The Nottingham Emmanuel School, West Bridgford

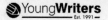

# Because Of Us...

Glancing around the once known Earth now lying in ruins, a shiver runs through my veins. Earth, the remains of extermination, the extermination we brought upon ourselves. We took it all for granted, we took everything for granted! Now it's all gone. Few survived, it's still not safe for those who have. Danger still lurks. Scavenging, searching, screaming, hoping someone will receive our cry for help. *Whoosh!* Not again. This is sure to be the last. There's a wave towering above the world as high as the clouds. It's over. Life is gone, because of us...

**Rhiannon Pearce (13)**
The Nottingham Emmanuel School, West Bridgford

# The Fall

Once, there was a group of friends who were on holiday. They were playing in the pool when suddenly, they saw it had started to get gloomy. Everyone looked up and saw a huge wave. They all started running, leaving all their belongings behind. Parents grabbed all their children and ran. All the cars started to fire their engines. The tsunami splashed onto the floor. People screamed, little children cried, people hung onto things, everybody was screaming. They had cuts and bruises, things were digging into them. Vehicles were floating, nobody had the strength to hold on...

**Hollie-May Jones (13)**
The Nottingham Emmanuel School, West Bridgford

# Twister

One day, there was a group of friends, Charlie, Ella, Freya and Tiago. They loved exploring. They went out every day running around the forest. Suddenly, it went dark. The clouds towered over the city. Howling winds at high speeds blew over everything in sight. The rain lashed down, it was horrendous. What was going on? No one knew. Something was happening, something bad. Sprinting, they got out of the forest as fast as they could, their lives depended on it. They saw something sweeping away anything in its path. What was it? They didn't know but nowhere was safe...

**Jessica Shaw (13)**
The Nottingham Emmanuel School, West Bridgford

# My Mysophobia

As I gazed at my hand, lost in thought, my memory foggy, my tears warmed, leaving a cold, hot sensation on my cheeks. My attention leaving my hands, I examined myself, noticing the rough and ripped clothes that gently brushed against my delicate skin. I was dirty. I couldn't stand it. I needed to get clean. The thought of germs lurking around bothered me. I grasped my sanitizer without hesitation. As I vigorously scrubbed, desperate to be clean again, my skin was irritated. I didn't care. "Argh, flip! It stings!" I shouted in agony. My mysophobia...

**Loretta Nkomo (13)**
The Nottingham Emmanuel School, West Bridgford

# Burning Down

As I'm running away like an uncontrollable cheetah, the hot flames burn the house like a piece of trash. Feeling trapped as I'm trying to escape from the stinky, burnt atmosphere spreading everywhere and becoming even more toxic, the blistering flames stalk me from behind and invade all my property. Every time I try to look back, my heart breaks into pieces like crumbs falling from a biscuit. Now what do I do? Where do I go? Now I'm trapped and disorientated, lonely like a wolf lost in the forest.
Hopeless.
Miserable.
Exasperated...

**Jennifer Quarcoopome (13)**
The Nottingham Emmanuel School, West Bridgford

# The Crumbling Depths Of Death

The world was closing in, the lights were going out and everyone everywhere was disappearing. There were rumbles as earth crashed down. I had to stay safe... but where? My hands were stained with grimy dirt and my fingertips were numb. My clothes were ragged and dropping as if they were soggy and clumped. The roofs tumbled and scattered around where my house once was. Clouds of dust floated around above my head. The air was shady and filled with regret. Tiny, frozen particles hit my face, the phone signal down, the Internet down, how could I find anyone now?

**Tiarnna Karim (14)**
The Nottingham Emmanuel School, West Bridgford

# The New NYC

Frozen. Trembling. Astonished. Everything around me frozen. No sign of heat. Cold bodies. Iced food. Frozen everything. Corpses frozen, lying on the remains of our city. New York is ruined. Icicles are daggers digging into my arms. I feel the frost building up within my bones. I see my house, my life, my memories. Gone forever. I walk into it. Ornaments stand there, shattered, filled with ice. I am immune, somehow. Why me? I stare into my dog's eyes, wishing for us both to just die and ascend to Heaven. "Please God, I am begging you, please..."

**Renai Rikki Dayes (13)**
The Nottingham Emmanuel School, West Bridgford

# Tortured Peace

Screams were all I could hear as the waves came charging towards us like soldiers. Running for dear life, the buildings that once stood tall and proud began to kneel down to the superior waves and the people around me continued to scurry away, yet still not sure where to go. Helicopters came swooping down to grab the most important people. They didn't care about me. Panting heavily, I couldn't continue any longer. The waves were too strong, they were too fast. I stopped, knowing it was over. Taking my last breath, the waves came washing over me...

**Trisha Taurai Saxby (13)**
The Nottingham Emmanuel School, West Bridgford

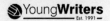
# Mother Nature

It was unexpected for Mother Nature to attack... to reclaim! England was the first to go, followed by China and many more but now it was the USA's time to fall. People tried to fight back but there was no point. Quickly, when one plant had been killed, another two grew back in its place. In the blink of an eye, plants were multiplying as fast as bacteria. Hiding, I watched as everyone trampled over each other for their lives, there was no point. *Growl!* How could I forget? If the plants had come back, so had the animals... "Argh!"

**Myles Peet (13)**
The Nottingham Emmanuel School, West Bridgford

# 2069

Global warming has caused disaster all over Earth. Walking around the city, not knowing what lies ahead, you could be squashed by a building, frozen to death or burnt to death, all depending on where you live in the world. Driving around the world, I get chills down my spine, buildings collapse all around me, the ground cracks beneath my car. I can't believe it. The president is creating a super secret space shuttle where everyone has to go to live. I rush into the shuttle. Little do I know that the president wanted this - the shuttle explodes...

**Maksymilian Reczkowski (13)**
The Nottingham Emmanuel School, West Bridgford

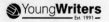

# The Start Of The End

Increasing day by day, the heat becomes unbearable as resources become scarcer by the day. Suddenly, a disease breaks out. Only five people are able to survive just the first day. Limited supplies. One of the fortunate survivors, Gorge, was able to survive the first day as he is immune! A small hut is all he has and some food and water. He walks into the devastation, four people remain. Then an enormous crack occurs! London is now isolated from the rest of the world. Zombies now rule the city. As resources are scarce, it's a fight until death...

**Connor Ford (13)**
The Nottingham Emmanuel School, West Bridgford

# The Solution

We thought we had found a solution to all wars, to stop all the criminals, but we had only made it worse. Genetically modified humans that could halt a plane with a single finger. Unprepared, they quickly fought back, realising the power they had over us. We were defenceless, they quickly seized our houses. We were powerless, they wiped out our families. Now, only a few are left. I, Tyler, regretfully had to wipe out my city in order to survive. Now I spend my days searching through the rubble for anything to keep me alive, but I'm not alone...

**Sam Casey (13)**
The Nottingham Emmanuel School, West Bridgford

# The Final Chance

It had arrived, the earthquake was devouring mankind's greatest inventions. Steve sprinted past the buildings. *Boom!* Another chunk gone from the doomed city. Steve didn't look back as he knew that it was the end. The earthquake was roaring with anger as the trembling remains of the city were being torn apart. "No!" Steve's foot was caught in the ground. The man screamed while the earthquake crushed the earth with its powerful foot. It surrounded him as he was begging to be released, then he fell through the earth...

**Qamar Akhtar (14)**
The Nottingham Emmanuel School, West Bridgford

# Where Is He?

I intended it to be a relaxing vacation, but it's all gone wrong. Looking through the glass, an 'illusion' is now reality. *Splat!* The glass is smashing, slowly, gently, until it caves in. "Run!" Everything's gone. Nothing but dirty water. *Where is he? Where is my brother?* Gone. Disappeared into thin air. Bruises all over my body, blood leaking from my body, the floor starts to shake. Is it another wave?
I am drowning. The water goes warm, my heart slowing. As my breathing stops, I find him...

**Adelia Hunter (13)**
The Nottingham Emmanuel School, West Bridgford

# Ellie And The Outrageous Earthquake

Discombobulated, Ellie searched for her freedom. Baffled, she trembled across the crystal clear floor. *Crack!* The glass floor chased Ellie as she ran to the concrete floor panicked, breathless, her life was going to be over. "I'm safe!" exclaimed Ellie, but she had forgotten that there was no one with her. Her family were way back in Germany. She tried to get in touch online with her parents but the Internet was demolished. She had nothing. Running back to her room, immediately, she locked the door and began to cry.

**Satvinder Kaur (14)**
The Nottingham Emmanuel School, West Bridgford

# Mission Revenge

Arrrghh! Help, we are going to drown. Run!
The next day...
Walking weakly, I gaze around and see bits of metal and rubble for miles. Flabbergasted, I realise that we need to do something about the evil mastermind who is living underground and creating catastrophes like earthquakes, floods and many more. This city is not made of money and unfortunately, we don't grow it on trees!
I look down and realise that I am drenched from the flood. I have nothing to dry myself off with and I have nowhere to sleep or live!

**Zara Brittain (12)**
The Nottingham Emmanuel School, West Bridgford

# The Last Survivor

What has happened? I don't know...

I look around and all I see is destruction and clutter everywhere. I must survive till the end, till I get rescued and taken to a safe city. Wait, where are my family? My sister, mum and dad - where have they gone? They must have been rescued... but how? When did they get rescued? I want to know what's happened.

I wander through the darkness, waiting. Waiting for a voice, the sound of a helicopter or something to rescue me.

Suddenly, I hear a crack. A crunch. A growl...

**Iola Hall (12)**
The Nottingham Emmanuel School, West Bridgford

# The Outbreak

The signals, the events, they all led up to one catastrophic disaster...

It was Pa. Pa was a foolish man. He was always so cautious until one night, his brain got a tumour that affected the way he acted and the way he was treated. Now look what's happened...

Something crashed. Pa went to look at it because it landed by his field. It had scarlet and purple spines that were intimidating to the eye. He took it to the scrapyard but it was too late, the infection patrolled across all of America. Disease, outbreak...

**Joe Bakewell (13)**
The Nottingham Emmanuel School, West Bridgford

# Destruction

"It's coming! Get out, get protected, get to safety!" Suddenly, an earthquake erupts, lightning forms and thunder roars in the sky. "Tony, come on! Get to safety!" A wall collapses and blocks him from his friends and family.

"Where are you?" He starts to move the rocks and the bricks. He sees a passage leading to the outside. A large fountain of water comes and floods the area. Struggling, he grabs onto a broken piece of building and climbs onto it, but he falls back into the flood...

**Ethan Crofts (13)**
The Nottingham Emmanuel School, West Bridgford

# Gone

All I own are these old, shrivelled clothes, not my house, not my wife, not my children. I remember when the first person got infected, no one took any notice then, did they? Now we face the consequences. I blame the scientists that got us into this mess. The remains of what used to be people, I see every day. I remember when seeing dead people wasn't the norm. I live in fear every day, hoping the virus won't find me like it did my family, watching them die a miserable, slow death. The pain haunts me to this day...

## Nila Mobashir (13)
The Nottingham Emmanuel School, West Bridgford

# And So It Came...

An apocalypse, who would have thought it? Caused by a gravitational wave that changed the sun. Now we live in a desert world with our star in a supernova state. Kind of funny, right? No! This caused the worst day of my life...
Tears ran down my face, leaving a line of clean cheek with the rest of it covered in ash. A plastic ring was in my hand, pulled from the corpse before me lying by a pillar of charcoaled wood. Her face disfigured and dead, I couldn't save her. I was afraid, too afraid to save my daughter.

**Broderick Liam Christman (14)**
The Nottingham Emmanuel School, West Bridgford

# The Zombie Apocalypse

"Breaking news! A disease was discovered late last night and the following day there was a zombie-like creature found. Police recommend staying indoors as now it has infected hundreds of people."
I was driving my car down the motorway and a zombie walked in front of my car and it rolled down into some woods. I was in the car whilst it was on its side, when I saw there were loads of them! I crawled to the fence and climbed over it. There was a young girl in one of the windows. She saw me and ran...

**Bailey Leek**
The Nottingham Emmanuel School, West Bridgford

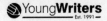

# The End

A thousand years ago, they said the end was near. Now the end is here and humans are on the verge of extinction and there's nothing we can do to stop it. Since the sun got closer and disease broke out, nearly ten thousand people have died from the solar flare and a million have been infected. The city I once played in has now been destroyed by the horrifying, monstrous creatures. I hear a scream. Suddenly, without hesitating, I run towards it. I am too late. There is a blood-sucking monster. I have to run...

**Tiago Pinheiro (13)**
The Nottingham Emmanuel School, West Bridgford

# Humanity Will Fall

I wake up feeling miserable and in pain. Something indestructible is going to happen, I can feel it. Suddenly, the ground starts to shake like thunder. I have to react quickly, but it's too late. When I step outside everything is destroyed. All I can see is the thick grey clouds lurking on top of me. I can't find my mum and dad. Maybe they died...
I don't know what to do.
The dust crushes my eyes. I look for other people; I look around, screaming and shouting.
The storm hits again...

**Ameer Adam Rabhe (12)**
The Nottingham Emmanuel School, West Bridgford

# The Islands

I watch the sun as it comes up in the morning, a safe glow of warmth. Now, it's never cold, since a scorching part of the sun flew at Earth. It melted our ice caps, flooded our homes. Now the last of us are trapped on islands, the last remains of the USA. I'm carrying a bag, old and broken. It contains all that I have. An old, portable radio, it never works but I'll wait in hope of contact. The sun is up now, its rays burning my back. *Bleep, bleep, bleep!* The radio crackles in my bag...

**Toby Clingan (13)**
The Nottingham Emmanuel School, West Bridgford

# Frozen

The clouds leaned over like trees. The bridge was broken, it had icicles hanging like rows of silver daggers. Smelling the deadly air burnt my nostrils. Puddles of frozen blood stared at me from the ground. As I walked away from murder, I was as terrified as a tiny mouse. "Run!" my brother told me so I ran, but I wanted my brother because he was all I had. "Argh! Help me!" Sharp blades of white pressed down. Suddenly, I had no hand on the left side. All I could see was blood and bones...

**Chelsea Beniston (13)**
The Nottingham Emmanuel School, West Bridgford

# The Disaster

Silently and cautiously, Sian Solomon sat watching the TV when all of a sudden, the ground started shaking in its boots and erupted with anger upon the people living in New York City. Sian quickly ducked for cover under a table until it stopped. When it did, the building (which was 10,000ft tall) started to collapse towards the quaking ground. She fell out of the window and slid down, dangling for her life until a prop from inside slid across the glass towards her, putting her life in even more danger...

**Kyren Skermer (13)**
The Nottingham Emmanuel School, West Bridgford

# Mission Catastrophe: The Test That Defines Mankind

I look around cautiously as all the memories come back. I used to work here at the lab, where we would test animals to see if we could enhance their strength and intelligence. They then became too brawny and intelligent to handle and they took over the world. I'm the only survivor as I hid and watched my workmates get eaten.

Suddenly I see a tiger, it could easily rip me into shreds. I stay quiet, thinking, *if I don't get out of here I will die.* It comes closer, closer...

**Cane Hyland-Wells**
The Nottingham Emmanuel School, West Bridgford

# Tornado Terror

I wake up. I hear the tornado sirens and people screaming, "It's here!"
My friend and I rush to the hideout, it is dark and cold so we turn the torch on. We have grabbed the survival kit my mum and dad packed. Then it all goes silent. The sirens and screams stop...
We climb our way out, then stop and look at each other.
"My mum and dad!"
We bolt to the kitchen and find them on the floor, dead. We walk slowly outside, there are only eight remaining...

**Lacie Harrop**
The Nottingham Emmanuel School, West Bridgford

# Rocks Of Doom

Waking up to broad daylight, I got up from my safe, warm place as usual and noticed stones on the floor. I looked out the window as people rushed out of buildings as though water was rapidly falling from a tap. Suddenly, rocks of doom buried my soul as the ground below me shook with terror. Horror chased my soul as I sprang back to life. Petrified, discombobulated and panicked, I was the only one left in a hateful world as I remained in the half-beaten building. I held onto my last breath...

**Toluwalase Adewumi (13)**
The Nottingham Emmanuel School, West Bridgford

# The Climate

My name is Johnathon. I have helped many people through my charity but now I wearily sit, thinking about how powerless I am now. From luxurious houses to the... ocean. Yes, climate change occurred and the sea levels rose but the most interesting thing is we are adapting, gaining scales, less tired of swimming, it is good. Every day, 'the wave' returns and adds a layer to the already high sea level. Every day, we have to train. Soon we might sleep and drown. Will we die or live?

**Mabad Ul-Hassan (13)**
The Nottingham Emmanuel School, West Bridgford

# The Collision

One day, I woke up to the news that there was a warning being broadcast that it would be the end of the world. I got up thinking it was just a person playing a prank, until I went outside and saw there was traffic everywhere and people were screaming! Then I got scared!
On the emergency broadcast it showed a view from space that all of the planets were going to collide. There was approximately 11 hours, 32 minutes and 17 seconds until the end... Was it the end?

**Logan Norman**
The Nottingham Emmanuel School, West Bridgford

# A Dystopian World

As I began in the new world, I travelled to America from Rome. I started to ask myself, "What's it like there?"

The roads were cracked, the cars were scratched, some rotten food bathed on the lava floor. "Oh my goodness!" I looked up to the sky, I saw a huge, and I mean huge, list of rules. I thought, *what is this world?* I saw a reflection, it was like a thousand eyes were looking at me... "Get me out of here!"

## Peace Animashaun (14)

The Nottingham Emmanuel School, West Bridgford

# The Grim Sky

Dear diary, it's the 28th of July, 2005. My deserted heart has no hope as the dead of the night gawks over me. The present has become a horror, the previous urban city has become no man's land like the trenches from 1939. My supplies are momentary. I currently possess bland, tinned food and bottled water but these resources will not last forever. My malnourished body is determined to survive another twenty-four hours. I will update my diary soon...

**Max Pawlowski (13)**
The Nottingham Emmanuel School, West Bridgford

# An Animal Catastrophe

It was the day that happiness grew inside of me. The day that I thought was going to be a day to remember. But then I realised the animals carried a disease that would kill us...

The animals freed themselves from their cages and started to spread the disease rapidly. Sarah yelled, "Holly, look behind you!"

"What is it?" I replied. The animals were after us to end us. Was this it? Was this the end of mankind?

**Tanzeela Tabrez (13)**
The Nottingham Emmanuel School, West Bridgford

# Blistering Hot

Gently, I opened the cold, creepy curtains to see a hot summer's day. Strangely, it felt hotter than normal but I got on with my daily routine. I stepped outside to see my skin blistering up, begging me to go back inside but I refused. The sun beamed down on me. "Watch out! Watch out!" I looked around as everyone dropped onto the floor, dead. I felt my body shaking as I shut my eyes and dropped...

**Zach Spindler (13)**
The Nottingham Emmanuel School, West Bridgford

# Death And Despair

Memories torment my brain as I relive the horror. Every time I think of it, I feel as though my mind is malfunctioning. I see the wave crashing before my eyes and the cacophony of shrieks overwhelming me. I start to sprint as a rumble trembles the earth as a warning. I frantically run out of time.
To this day, I'm yet to find the strength hidden within. Anything in its path was demolished and destroyed. People on the beach had already been taken prisoner and were inevitably drowned in their own tears of sorrow and fright. Despair sank in...

**Olivia Grace Harding (13)**
The Samworth Church Academy, Mansfield

# The End Of The World

I engulfed the West Coast. I sensed the bitter taste of danger lurking in the mouths of the remaining survivors. In the opposite direction, my sister was making landfall quicker than an eagle feasting upon its prey. Spiralling out of control, feeding on the houses and people below, my mother arched her back as she looked down, satisfied with our work. I let out the most piercing cacophony. Then silence. Out of nowhere, my father swept in across the south of the globe. United we stood, destroying everything within our path.

**Kady Weedop (13)**
The Samworth Church Academy, Mansfield

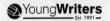

# A Dream Became Reality

I tried to recall my memories. I had dreamt the same dream. I lay solemnly, staring straight towards the light that peered round from under the lampshade. The dream had consisted of the tsunami echoing the cacophony of screams as my mum was slowly let into the desperate, thrashing wave making its way through but I never got to see the end. As I came back to reality, I could hear the noise of the waves crashing as if threatening me. Surrounding me was nothing. The place I used to call my home, the place I now call nothing.

**Imogen Hursthouse (13)**
The Samworth Church Academy, Mansfield

# The Sun Still Smiles

Everyone is dead apart from me. Somehow, I survived. The sun still smiles through with me but that doesn't change the smell of burnt flesh lingering in the air. Next to the bodies lie clothes incinerated. My surroundings are disfigured and unrecognisable. My life is now a continuous video game, there are so many paths I could take. I could savour every moment or die alone, either way no one would know so I'm going to savour every moment because tomorrow could be my last...

**Arabella Neve Radford (13)**
The Samworth Church Academy, Mansfield

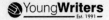
# Fate

Exhausted, I trudged through the obliterated village. Buildings groaned in pain as their bodies crumbled onto the overgrown ground like the flesh melting from the zombies. Belongings were covered in a thick layer of dust as I manoeuvered around them. *Why am I afraid to touch them? It's instinct, I suppose.* My heavy footsteps matched the feeling in my heart as they echoed down the hallway. There. I crept closer, unable to stop myself from sinking my teeth into the human's already mutilated flesh. Now they would suffer like me, their human mind would be trapped in a zombie's body.

**Kiera Flynn (12)**
Wilsthorpe School, Long Eaton

# The Haze

Space weather. Something mankind had never had to deal with... until now. Pollution and lack of action had all but killed the globe, meaning the illustrious foe could reach its long tendrils into Earth. Three strikes. That's all it took, and humanity was reduced to a few scattered survivors, most likely ginger as we redheads had a stronger, superior gene. Now the silence was almost deafening. Then a shriek pierced the quiet. A sound of distant screams and a red haze flashed across the sky, illuminating the death-corrupted landscape of a once life-filled Earth.

**Alex Twigg (12)**
Wilsthorpe School, Long Eaton

# Why Me?

I sit watching the news report. *What if I get sent over?* They've been turned into monsters by the radiation! All these years we've believed that the radiation isn't poisonous. They lied to us! My commander walks in, turning the TV off, he shouts at us to get on the plane. My heart sinks as I apprehensively line up with the others...
"Wow," I whisper as the plane lands and we all file out of it. The landscape is barely recognisable, everything is destroyed and everything seems... dead. Then I see them. They are coming for us...

**Hannah Jenkins (13)**
Wilsthorpe School, Long Eaton

# The End

I remember that day. The day I lost everything. Everything has changed. Now, there is no land, only water. After the scorching, the floods came, drowning anyone who couldn't swim. I'm lucky. Well, not really. I survived but lost everything and everyone. I try not to think about it. The only person I know in this place is my best friend. Right now, I'm with her. We are talking, now her eyes are filling with fright. "What is that?" she whispers. I turn and I see it. Deafening screams fill the air. Another wave. A tsunami no one can survive...

**Ruby Davies (11)**
Wilsthorpe School, Long Eaton

# The Flood Of The Farm

Everywhere I look, water. It's rising, and fast. The farm, the animals, what's happening? I'm alone, all alone. The water is filling up. I won't be able to breathe soon. Panic fills my mind, thoughts gushing in one ear and out the other. Quick-thinking comes in handy at this point. I swiftly wrap the rope around the old-fashioned beams and, as if it were an action movie, I jump off the hay bales and onto the stacked-up ladders, being extremely careful not to fall off the rope, far down into the depths of nothingness below. This could be it...

**Melissa Louise Bowers (12)**
Wilsthorpe School, Long Eaton

# The Unspoken

What are these monsters? What are they doing here? What do they want? Their disgusting acid-filled spots, their inhuman speed and shape, ripping the hearts out of innocent people and corrupting them for their own use. Blood and acidic puddles live everywhere, be cautious of your steps! Their supersonic hearing means the quietest whispers they hear, a breath of relief they hear, a step they hear. Only a few people live, most of them enemies in a race to be the last one alive, so they can finally be the rulers of the world, but I won't let them...

**Alex D'Arcy (13)**
Wilsthorpe School, Long Eaton

# Struck By Death

Terror, fear, death. It all happened so fast. I was sat in my bedroom when *boom!* It hit us hard. The hurricane had been predicted for a week but nobody prepared themselves for what was about to happen. The torrential rain started an hour before the screams. The windows smashed and the roof blew completely off. I heard my mum and sister screaming downstairs. I tried to get to them but my legs were trapped under something. Silence. The hurricane stopped, but then started again. I felt a bang on my head. Darkness. Had death really struck me?

**Amelia Parker (12)**
Wilsthorpe School, Long Eaton

# Perfect Paradise

Death. I could see it, smell it and practically taste it. I recoiled in disgust at the sight of mangled bodies littering the hard, damp, destroyed concrete. This wasn't what they deserved. They didn't deserve to be forgotten, to be left on the ground for the seagulls to peck at for an evening meal, to be dead. This wasn't what I had in mind for a 'perfect paradise'. Shineria, a place with a scorching sun. A place with so much excitement and wonder. I hoped for normality, to escape the world, but I got this. I wish I never went.

**Scarlet Burnell (12)**
Wilsthorpe School, Long Eaton

# Withers Lake

A soft blanket of snow lay spread across the barn floor, covering the hay as if it were eating it alive. Whilst the crisp air howled between the branches of the few brittle oak trees surrounding us, thirst dried our throats and the scent of sweet apple orchards was hypnotising. The lit moon shone over our faces like a veil and we had found ourselves lost. A spring caught the corner of my eye, the reflection giving me a boost of life. Tears welled in my eyes. "Water!" I murmured. My only and last hope. "Blue, we've made it!"

**Phoebe Warwick (11)**
Wilsthorpe School, Long Eaton

# Survival

Alone. Abandoned. Deserted. Only a few hundred people left alive over the globe and at least 20,000 of the infected. I live in a secret bunker filled with food, medicine, water, weapons and all the survival equipment I could ever want. Yet, the food is running out and I will have to venture into the adjusted Earth with animals and the infected running wild. The disease came from outer space in the form of dark matter and can either kill or take over a person's brain. I open up the hatch and cautiously progress outside, but will I return?

**Eli Enzo Beard (11)**
Wilsthorpe School, Long Eaton

# Helplessly And Hopelessly

I was in London, Big Ben had just collapsed. Everything was on fire. People were running around screaming hysterically. It seemed impossible to survive but I tried. I looked at the London Eye, stood proudly, illuminating the sky with fire. Suddenly, someone pushed me and I went plummeting to the ground. A loud bang deafened me for a minute as I glanced back at the towering Ferris wheel. It was gone. Still on the ground, helplessly lying there, someone stood on me. My ears began to ring. I closed my eyes. London was never the same again...

**Isobel Jane Eyre (11)**
Wilsthorpe School, Long Eaton

# The Darkness

Darkness consumed Earth as the sun and stars went out. I was shaking, I couldn't see a thing. Now, five months later, I'm used to the dark. The only source of light is fire. As soon as the darkness came, all the electricity and power went out. Bit by bit, people started to starve and die, some even went insane and killed others and themselves. Nobody knows why the stars and the sun went out. There are hundreds of theories but that's all they are, theories. My family didn't survive, they all went insane. I had to run away.

**Daisy Smith (13)**
Wilsthorpe School, Long Eaton

# Fiery Passion

The world was on fire. A voice screamed inside my head, the voice of fear, of horror and of anger. Anger for myself, my family and my friends against the evil people who did this, the selfish, ignorant ones that came before. It was them who caused this with their careless burning of gases they knew would poison the world. Didn't anyone care? Didn't anyone try to stop this? They knew. They knew but they didn't care, didn't care about us, about our world that they've destroyed. I hate them with a fiery passion.

**Zoe King (12)**
Wilsthorpe School, Long Eaton

# The Uprise

I still remember being on that train on that day...
I was on my way to London to see my family. I was
listening to music when it happened. I had just
picked up my phone to change the song when the
train floor began to shake. As I looked up, an army
of military troops stormed in, shooting wherever
they saw life. I dived into the toilet cubicle and
locked the door, praying no one saw me...
It's been three days, I'm still here with no food, no
water, nothing. The world is breaking apart. This is
the uprising...

**Amélie Tuck (13)**
Wilsthorpe School, Long Eaton

# Stronger Than Us

They finally came. The world has changed forever. We have all been lied to! The human race is a joke. We are the weakest creatures out there. The houses have been crushed, the forests have been burnt, humanity has been burnt to a crisp. Nobody is safe from these mutants. They fly in the sky and swim in the water. Nobody can save us. They bite and tear you apart limb from limb. All around you, you can hear bones cracking and skin ripping. You hear cackles from the cave, they don't sound human. They are mutant pigeons...

**Sophie Louise Morris (13)**
Wilsthorpe School, Long Eaton

# Gone Forever

The door flung open, revealing what we had all been hoping to see. Mother stepped in, bewildered and confused. My eyes brimmed with tears. I processed seeing her face once again, tears were now streaming down my cheeks. Precious Mother, who I had struggled to say goodbye to, was now stood right in front of me in the flesh, not just in my dreams. She edged towards me, trembling all over. I wrapped my arms around her in a warm embrace. She was cold and distant. Her soul had been left behind. Dead inside, gone forever...

## May Longmoor (12)
Wilsthorpe School, Long Eaton

# A Thousand Ghost Faces

I'm walking underneath the city scars, car lights zoom past me, the bitter air sends a shiver down my spine and looking up at the moon, I see a cloud move in from the north. Not just any cloud though, a green cloud. And it's approaching rapidly. I look over to the north and the cloud is much bigger. The fluorescent moon is no longer visible and I can only just about see the stars. People start to get out of their cars and a murmur starts to spread around the street. Then I see it. A thousand ghost faces...

**Maisie Booker (12)**
Wilsthorpe School, Long Eaton

# The Swim

This was it. My last shot. My last decision. My last chance. I wasn't ever the brave type. In fact, I wasn't the 'type' at all. The type that helped in the worst situations or the type that one day would save the world from its lowest point in history. The waves crashed. It was almost like a scream of desperation, discomposure, but ambition at the same time. The one thing I knew was that I had to save my dad. I swam until my arms were in agony. Then I saw his hat. Just the hat...

**Yasmin Jade Johnson (13)**
Wilsthorpe School, Long Eaton

# The Crater

It was like a bomb went off in my head. The deafening blast shook the world. A shockwave blanketed Earth and brought buildings down to their knees. A crater the size of China appeared in the Pacific Ocean while people screamed in complete fear of the unknown. Things and even people began to lift into the air as Earth was knocked off its axis and gravity lost all purpose. The scene of disturbing chaos on the streets stained my mind. I couldn't see any hope at all, I could see no end...

**Izzy Johnson (13)**
Wilsthorpe School, Long Eaton

# YOUNG WRITERS INFORMATION

We hope you have enjoyed reading this book – and that you will continue to in the coming years.

If you're a young writer who enjoys reading and creative writing, or the parent of an enthusiastic poet or story writer, do visit our website **www.youngwriters.co.uk**. Here you will find free competitions, workshops and games, as well as recommended reads, a poetry glossary and our blog.

If you would like to order further copies of this book, or any of our other titles, then please give us a call or order via your online account.

Young Writers
Remus House
Coltsfoot Drive
Peterborough
PE2 9BF
(01733) 890066 / 898110
info@youngwriters.co.uk

Join in the conversation!

 YoungWritersUK           @YoungWritersCW